RIDE

Virginia A. Arnold

SENIOR AUTHORS
Virginia A. Arnold
Carl B. Smith

LITERATURE CONSULTANTS
Joan I. Glazer
Margaret H. Lippert

READING
EXPRESS
MACMILLAN

Macmillan Publishing Company
New York

Collier Macmillan Publishers
London

D1160102

ACKNOWLEDGMENTS

The publisher gratefully acknowledges permission to reprint the following copyrighted material:

"The Merry-Go-Round" by Electa Clark from CHILDREN'S ACTIVITIES. Reprinted by permission, HIGHLIGHTS FOR CHILDREN, INC. Columbus, Ohio.

From "Riding in An Airplane" by Dorothy W. Baruch. Reprinted by permission of Bertha Klausner International Literary Agency, Inc.

Cover Design: Bass and Goldman Associates

Illustration Credits: Lulu Delacre, 23–27; Marla Frazee, 9; Laurie Jean Jordan, 21; Gordon Kibbie, 41–46; Loretta Lustig, 5–8; Moira & Colin Maclean, 11–15; Bob Shein, 17–20, 47; Vicki Wehrman, 4, 10, 16, 22, 28, 34, 40.

Cover Photo: Animals, Animals: © Ken Lewis.

Photo Credits: © Robert Lee II, 29–33, 35–39.

Macmillan Publishing Company
866 Third Avenue
New York, N.Y. 10022
Collier Macmillan Canada, Inc.

Printed in the United States of America

ISBN 0-02-160010-4

9 8 7 6 5 4 3 2

Contents

PREPARING FOR READING

Learning Vocabulary

Listen.

B b

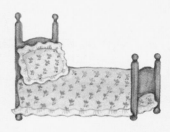

Read.

1. The boy rides.
2. The boy rides up.
3. The boy rides down.

the   boy   rides   up   down

The Boy Rides

The boy rides.
The boy rides up.

The boy rides up, up, up.

The boy rides down.
The boy rides down, down, down.

The Swing

How do you like to go up in a swing,
  Up in the air so blue?
Oh, I do think it the pleasantest thing
  Ever a child can do!

Robert Louis Stevenson

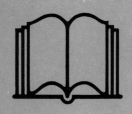

PREPARING FOR READING

Learning Vocabulary

Listen.

G g

Read.

1. The <u>girl</u> rides up.

2. The girl <u>can</u> <u>ride</u> down.

3. The girl can ride <u>and</u> ride.

girl   can   ride   and

The Girl and Boy Ride

The girl can ride.
The boy can ride.
The boy and girl can ride.

The girl rides up and up.
The girl rides down and down.

The boy rides up and up.
The boy rides down and down.

The girl and boy can ride up and down.
The girl and boy can ride and ride.

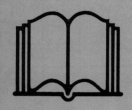

PREPARING FOR READING

Learning Vocabulary

Listen.

M   m

Read.

1. The <u>man</u> can ride.

2. Can the man <u>go</u> up?

man   go

UP AND DOWN

Can the man go up?
The man can go up and up.

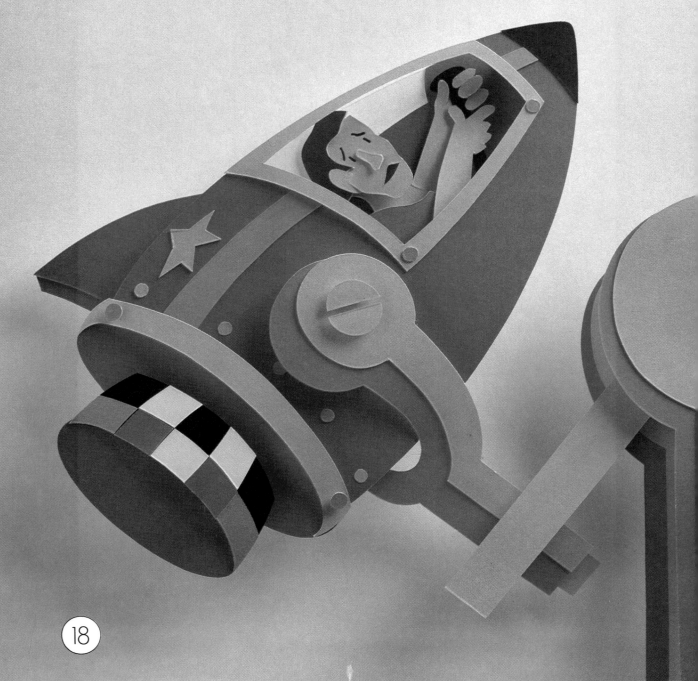

Can the man go down?
The man can go down, down, down.

Can the man go up and down?
Can the man go down and up?
The man can!

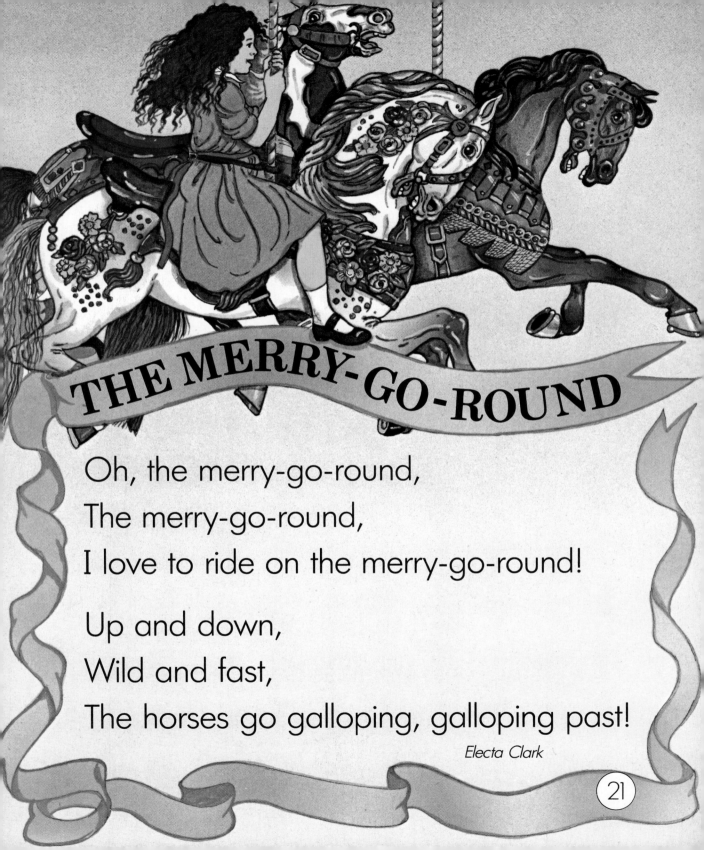

THE MERRY-GO-ROUND

Oh, the merry-go-round,
The merry-go-round,
I love to ride on the merry-go-round!

Up and down,
Wild and fast,
The horses go galloping, galloping past!

Electa Clark

21

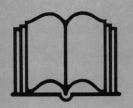

PREPARING FOR READING

Learning Vocabulary

Listen.

L l

Read.

1. The fish likes to ride.
2. The fish likes to jump.
3. The fish likes to ride now.

fish   likes   to   jump   now

The Fish Rides

The fish likes to ride.

Now the fish rides up and up.

The fish likes to jump.

Now the fish can jump up and down.

The fish likes to ride down.

Now the fish rides down and down.

The fish likes to ride.

The fish likes to jump.

The fish likes to ride and jump.

PREPARING FOR READING

Learning Vocabulary

Listen.

H h

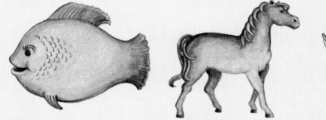

Read.

1. The man can <u>help</u>.

2. The <u>woman</u> can help <u>Nan</u>.

3. Nan can go <u>on</u> the <u>plane</u>.

help woman Nan on plane

Nan
Rides

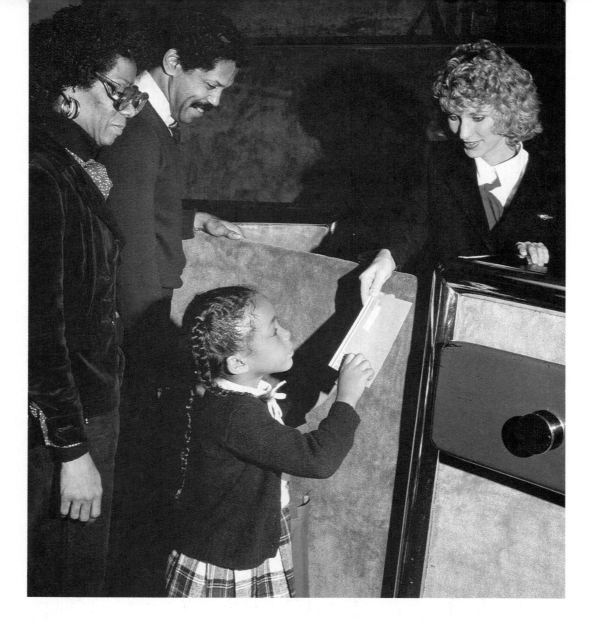

Nan likes to ride on the plane.

The woman likes to help.

The woman can help Nan.

Now Nan and the woman ride down.
Nan and the woman ride to the plane.

Nan likes the woman.

The woman likes to help Nan.

Nan can go on the plane now.

Nan likes to go up on the plane.

Nan likes to ride on the plane.

PREPARING FOR READING

Learning Vocabulary

Listen.

S   s

Read.

1. <u>See</u> the plane.

2. The woman can <u>read</u>.

3. The man <u>helps</u> the woman.

see   read   helps

On the Plane

Nan likes the plane.

Nan can see down.

Nan can see up.

The man helps on the plane.
The man helps Nan.
Nan helps the man.

Nan can read on the plane.

Nan can read to the woman.

Nan likes to read.

Nan can see and read.

Nan rides down on the plane.

Now Nan can go.

PREPARING FOR READING

Learning Vocabulary

Listen.

man

Read.

1. Can't you see the plane?

2. I can't see the plane.

3. Can't you see the dog?

4. I can see a dog now.

can't   you   I   dog   a

The Dog and the Jump

The dog likes to ride on a plane.

Can I ride on the plane?

You can ride.
Can you jump?

A dog can jump.

A dog likes to jump.

I can ride up and jump down.

The dog rides up on the plane.

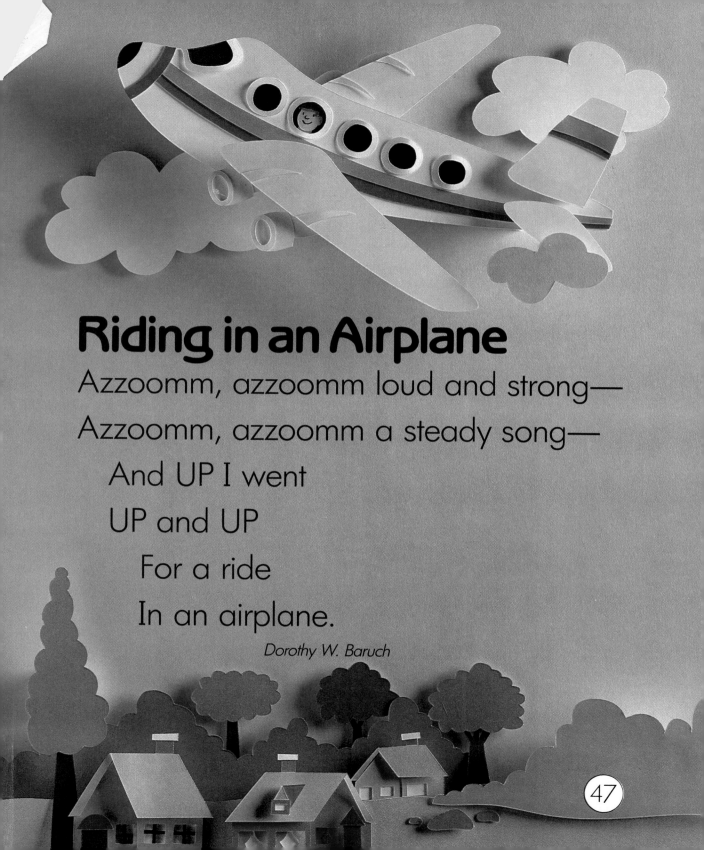

Riding in an Airplane

Azzoomm, azzoomm loud and strong—

Azzoomm, azzoomm a steady song—

    And UP I went

    UP and UP

      For a ride

      In an airplane.

Dorothy W. Baruch

Word List

The Boy Rides
6. the
   boy
   rides
   up
8. down

The Girl and Boy Ride
12. girl
    can
    ride
    and

Up and Down
18. man
    go

The Fish Rides
24. fish
    likes
    to
    now
25. jump

Nan Rides
30. Nan
    on
    plane
    woman
    help

On the Plane
36. see
37. helps
38. read

The Dog and the Jump
42. dog
    a
    I
    you
44. can't